Spring

SPY IT! SCORE IT!

Introduction

Spring is the season between winter and summer, and in the UK, it spans the entire months of March, April and May. It signals the start of everything coming back to life – trees begin to grow buds, and then leaves; daffodils and crocuses begin to shoot up from beneath the ground, and some vegetables like spring greens and spring onions start to appear.

It's also the time for new life! Many baby animals are born in spring, so you might be lucky enough to see some newborn lambs and calves if you're out and about near a farm. Wild animals like foxes and rabbits have their babies in spring too, so keep your eyes peeled for their newborn offspring if you're out in the countryside.

So, wherever you are, and whatever you're up to, get spotting all things spring!

How to use your i-SPY book

Keep your eyes peeled for the i-SPYs in the book.

If you spy it, score it by ticking the circle or star.

Items with a star are difficult to spot so you'll have to search high and low to find them.

Once you score 1000 points, send away for your super i-SPY certificate. Follow the instructions on page 64 to find out how.

New arrivals

There are a lot of newborn animals to look out for in spring. Many animals give birth to their young at this time of year, so that they have time to grow big before the winter.

Lamb

During spring, fields are filled with adorable lambs, who stay with their mothers until they are weaned at the end of summer. Female sheep are called ewes, and usually give birth to one or two lambs at a time.

15 POINTS

Calf

The main calving season in the UK lasts from late February until May. All calves must be given ear tags within a short time of being born, which helps them to be identified and recorded.

20 POINTS

Piglet

A female pig can give birth to up to fourteen piglets at a time. Pigs are very social creatures and like to live in family groups. Although they are the most commonly farmed animal, you may have to go to a farmyard or farm park to see a piglet.

30 POINTS

TOP SPOT!

Foal

Newborn horses are called foals. They stand up within an hour of being born, though their legs are very wobbly at first. They usually stay with their mothers for at least six months, so you may see them in a field together.

25 POINTS

Kid

A baby goat is called a kid. Goats usually give birth to twins or triplets in the spring. Their mothers recognise them by their voice and their smell, rather than by how they look.

40 POINTS

TOP SPOT

4

Chick

A fluffy yellow chick will grow up to be a hen or cockerel. You might see one in a farmyard, a city farm or in someone's garden.

20 POINTS

Duckling

Look out for mother ducks being followed by their broods of fluffy ducklings from April onwards. The ducklings stay with their mother for about two months, learning what is safe for them to eat.

15 POINTS

Gosling

Young geese are known as goslings until their fluffy down is replaced by feathers. Look for them near water, such as park ponds, small lakes or wetlands, and score for seeing any type of gosling.

25 POINTS

New arrivals

Cygnet

You might see a grey, fluffy cygnet getting a ride on its parent's back. These young swans soon get too big for that, but they'll stay with their parents for up to a year after they are born.

15 POINTS

Tadpole

Frogs and toads begin life as tadpoles, which you can look for in ponds, ditches and around lake edges in April. They start off with a small, oval head and a wiggly tail. As they grow bigger, the tail is absorbed into the body and two legs develop. They finally hop out of the water as tiny froglets or toadlets.

20 POINTS

Fledgling

A fledgling is a young bird that has grown feathers and is ready to learn to fly. If you see a young bird sitting on the ground, it may have just left the nest for the first time and be getting ready for its first flight. Its parents will probably be nearby, keeping a watchful eye on it.

40 POINTS

TOP SPOT

ox cub

xes are born in litters of
bout five, in underground
sts called dens. They start to
nture out when they are
ur weeks old and still small,
look out for them from April
wards. They love to play fight
ith their brothers and sisters.

TOP SPOT!

50 POINTS

Baby rabbit (kitten)

Wild rabbits are common
all around the UK. You will
see them in fields, parks and
even grass verges. Female
rabbits can produce a litter
of between three and seven
young every month during
the breeding season, so
you have a good chance of
spotting one!

15 POINTS

Weather

The weather during spring can be varied, but it gets warmer as the season progresses and the days become longer.

Sunshine

The sunshine can start to feel quite warm from early spring. It helps to make the trees, plants and grass grow.

Showers

April is well known for its rain showers, though these might happen during other months too.

5 POINTS

Wind

Low pressure can bring unsettled weather to the UK in the spring, meaning that it can get windy.

5 POINTS

Hail

Hail falls as little balls of ice, which are formed from water that is frozen high up in the clouds.

20 POINTS

In the sky

Each day during spring, the sun sets about two minutes later than it did the day before. There are different things to look for in the sky as the season progresses and the days get longer and warmer.

Cancer the Crab

In early spring, the evenings are still dark enough for stargazing. Look out for Cancer the Crab in March and April. If you use binoculars, you will see that some of the stars are actually clusters of stars.

20 POINTS

Leo the Lion

Leo the Lion can also be seen in March and April. It is easy to spot – look for it just below the saucepan-shaped Plough.

15 POINTS

Virgo

You might have to stay up late to spot the constellation of Virgo, as this one is best viewed in May.

20 POINTS

10

Full Moon

Every 29 or 30 days, we can see the whole of the Moon reflecting the light from the Sun. Native Americans gave the full Moons names according to what was happening in nature at the same time of year. The Worm Moon is the full Moon in March, the Pink Moon is in April and the Flower Moon is in May. Score points for any that you spy.

10 POINTS

Vapour trail

If you see an aeroplane flying across the sky on a clear day, it might leave two long straight lines of cloud behind it. These are vapour trails or contrails, which are created by the condensation of water around pollutants from the engine.

10 POINTS

In the sky

Hot air balloon

Hot air balloons carry people in a basket beneath an enormous balloon. The air inside the balloon is heated by a flame, which makes it rise. The best time of day to fly is in the calm early morning or evening, so you are more likely to spot one as the days get longer.

TOP SPOT!

50 POINTS

Paraglider or Paramotor

These flying machines allow you to fly like a bird! They both have a canopy like a parachute. The paraglider relies on pockets of warm air to stay airborne and needs to be launched off the side of a hill, while the paramotor has a motor, which gives the pilot more control over where they can take off and where they can fly. Score for seeing either.

TOP SPOT!

50 POINTS

Kite

Colourful kites of all shapes and sizes can be seen in parks, on beaches and in other open spaces on windy days.

15 POINTS

Drone

You might hear the buzz of a drone before you see it. These small, remote-controlled flying devices often carry a camera for taking amazing aerial photographs and films.

25 POINTS

Cumulus cloud

This fluffy cloud looks like a ball of cotton wool and is a sign of good weather.

Cirrus cloud

This wispy cloud is formed very high up in the air and is made of ice crystals. Although it is associated with blue sky and sunshine, it is usually a sign that the weather is about to change.

Nimbostratus cloud

This dark layer of grey cloud is the type that drops rain on us.

owering trees and shrubs

es and shrubs burst into life in the spring. Beautiful flowers
ng colour to our gardens, parks, pavements and hedgerows,
d provide nectar and pollen for insects.

azel

azel trees produce catkins
late winter and early
ring. These are clusters of
y, yellow petal-less flowers
hich dangle from small
ranches arranged along a
entral stem. You will find
azel trees in woodland
nd hedgerows.

25 POINTS

Goat willow

Goat willow is a small tree that
grows in wet ground such as
ditches, though you can also find it
in gardens. The catkins appear in
late winter and are grey and fluffy
like a cat's paw, which is why they
are also called pussy willow. By
March the flowers are fully open
and yellow, and attract lots of
pollinating insects.

TOP SPOT!

30 POINTS

Flowering trees and shrubs

Camellia

This is one of the first shrubs of the year to flower. It has dark, glossy green leaves and brightly coloured red, pink or white flowers. Look for it in gardens and parks.

20 POINTS

Gorse

This prickly shrub grows wild on heaths, coasts and open grassland. It flowers throughout the spring, with small yellow blooms that smell of coconut.

20 POINTS

Forsythia

Even though this garden shrub only flowers for a short time in March, you can't miss it because it is completely covered in bright yellow flowers. The small flowers are star-shaped, with four petals.

10 POINTS

Amelanchier

This tree blossoms with small, white, star-shaped flowers in March and has bronze-coloured leaves in spring. Look out for it in gardens.

 25 POINTS

Flowering currant

This shrub is native to North America. It is also a popular garden plant in the UK because of its fragrant dark pink flowers in March and April.

 30 POINTS

Cherry

Cherry blossom is one of the most common and recognisable blossoms. You will often see cherry trees lining a road or path covered in pink or white blossom during April.

 10 POINTS

Flowering trees and shrubs

Hawthorn

You may see hawthorn growing as an individual tree, or in a hedgerow along a roadside or the edge of a field. It is covered in blossom during late April and May. The flowers are usually white or pink, with five round petals. The blossom appears after the leaves have started to open, which will help you to identify it.

25 POINTS

Appl

Look out for appl blossom in May. Th flowers grow in cluster They have five petals an are usually white with hint of pink

20 POINTS

Magnolia

Magnolia trees produce exotic-looking tulip or star-shaped flowers in May. They can be pink or white, and often have a lovely smell. The trees can be large or small, and you will usually find them in parks and gardens.

15 POINTS

Wisteria

Wisteria is a climbing plant that you are most likely to see growing up the front of a house. In May it produces lots of flowers on long stems called pendants. The flowers are a light bluish-purple colour and have a strong scent.

20 POINTS

Elder

Elder is a shrub-like tree that grows in woods and hedgerows. It produces large sprays of tiny white flowers towards the end of May. The flowers can be used to make elderflower cordial, but you need to be sure that it is elderflower that you're picking if you want to make cordial yourself.

35 POINTS

Rhododendron

These shrubs produce big, bold flowers in late spring. Look out for them in large gardens or parks, or in woodland. The flowers are usually pink or purple, but you might see other colours too.

20 POINTS

Flowering trees and shrubs

Lilac

The flowers on this small tree can be lilac in colour, but also white or pink. The flower stems have lots of tiny flowers with a strong fragrance. Look out for them in gardens in late spring.

25 POINTS

Laburnum

These ornamental trees produce lots of small, bright yellow flowers on long, drooping stems. They flower in late spring and are a common sight in gardens.

15 POINTS

Flowers

There are more and more flowers to look out for as spring progresses. If you don't see them in your neighbourhood, you might see some of them in your local garden centre.

Pansy

Look for pansies in flower beds, containers and hanging baskets. They flower from winter into spring in a variety of colour combinations.

10 POINTS

Crocus

Crocuses start flowering in late winter but you will still see them in spring. They grow low to the ground and are usually purple, yellow or white.

10 POINTS

Flowers

Daffodil

You might see these flowers as early as February. They grow from bulbs planted in the ground or in pots, and are a cheery sight at the end of winter. They are usually bright yellow, but some varieties are white or have an orange centre.

 5 POINTS

Miniature narcissus

These dwarf daffodils grow in clumps and flower at the same time as the larger daffodils.

 10 POINTS

Hyacinth

Hyacinths have a strong fragrance. They can be grown indoors, but will flower outside in March.

5 POINTS

Grape hyacinth

Also known as muscari, these small plants have lots of tiny bluish-purple flowers that look like bunches of grapes. They are often grown in pots, and flower in March.

25 POINTS

Daisy

Daisies are tiny yellow and white flowers that grow wild amongst the grass. Their name comes from 'day's eye', since they open out when the sun comes up and close over at night. Score double points if you make a daisy chain necklace.

5 POINTS

Dandelion

This is another wild flower that grows amongst the grass. Dandelion gets its name from the French for lion's tooth! This bright yellow flower appears from March onwards.

5 POINTS

Flowers

Primrose

Wild primroses are creamy-yellow, but you may see other colours in parks and gardens, including white, pink, red, purple and blue. They grow low to the ground in shaded areas, and flower throughout the spring.

○ **10** POINTS

Tulip

Tulips grow from bulbs planted in the soil and have a single cup-shaped flower with large petals. They are usually red, pink, yellow or white, and you will find them in parks and gardens in March and April.

○ **10** POINTS

Wild garlic

You might smell wild garlic before you see it. It carpets woodland floors and has spherical clusters of delicate white flowers that appear in April.

☆ **35** POINTS

Bluebell

Bluebells turn woodland into a magical sight when they carpet the ground in April and May. You might see some individual plants in a park or garden too.

 20 POINTS

Wood sorrel

Look for these low-growing flowers in woodland and under hedges in April and May. Their white or pink petals have lilac veins on them. The leaves are made up of three parts called 'lobes', which fold up at night to make a tent shape.

TOP SPOT!

 40 POINTS

ris

hese flowers are usually yellow
hen they grow in the wild in
narshland and around lake edges.
ometimes you will see purple irises
n parks and gardens.
hey flower in late
pring. Score for
potting either colour.

 20 POINTS

Breeding birds

All of these bird species migrate from other countries to the UK to breed. They arrive in the spring to take advantage of the climate and food that is available here. In some of the species, the male has more colourful feathers than the female. This is so that the female is camouflaged when she is sitting on the eggs in the nest.

Chiffchaff

This is one of the first migrants to arrive. From early March, listen out for the *chiff-chaff* sound it makes when perched at the top of a tree, which is how it got its name.

35 POINTS

Swallow

Swallows arrive in March and are a common sight across the whole country. They spend most of their time flying around, swooping to catch insects. Look out for their distinctive red throats and long, forked tails.

15 POINTS

Blackcap

It's easy to see how this bird got its name. It is the male blackcap which has black feathers on its head; the female's head is a chestnut colour. They can be found in woodland and also parks where there are plenty of trees.

35 POINTS

Puffin

With its large, colourful beak, black and white plumage, and bright orange legs, there is no mistaking a puffin! These birds are not easy to find, however, as they only breed along certain parts of the UK's coast. They arrive in March or April, and by the summer they have flown back out to sea where they spend the rest of the year.

50 POINTS

TOP SPOT!

Breeding birds

Redstar[t]

Look out for the male redstart i[n] wooded areas or near stream[s] from April onwards. You migh[t] confuse it for a robin, but th[e] redstart also has an orange ta[il] and a black face[.]

40 POINTS

Wheatear

These birds feed on the ground, so you might see them hopping around open grassland or farmland. The male has a bluish-grey back with a pale orange front and a dark stripe across its eye, while the female's back is brown. Score for spotting either.

40 POINTS

Whitethroat

Both the male and female whitethroat are brown with a white throat, though the male also has a grey head. They breed all over the UK, in the countryside and in towns.

35 POINTS

Breeding birds

Nesting box

You will spot nesting boxes high up in trees and on buildings, in gardens, parks and woods. They attract small birds such as robins, blue tits and house sparrows. Score an extra 10 points if you spy a bird going in or coming out of a nesting box.

10 POINTS

Bird building a nest

Some birds prefer to build their own nests. If you see one flying around in early spring with bits of twig or moss in its beak, you can be sure it's building a nest nearby.

25 POINTS

Bird sitting on a nest

Birds build their nests in all sorts of places –
trees, bushes, reeds, cliff faces and even in
buildings. Some of the easiest ones to spot are
those on the ground. Wherever the nest is, be careful not
to disturb the bird sitting on it.

25 POINTS

Bird carrying insects

Later on in the spring, once the chicks
have hatched, the adults get busy
gathering food for them. Watch out
for birds flying backwards and
forwards. See if they are carrying
insects in their beaks,
which they will be taking
back to the nest to feed
to their young.

30 POINTS

Breeding birds

Nest box webcam

Some people fit webcams into nesting boxes so they can watch all the activity inside. You might see some footage on a television programme; otherwise you can find it online. Try searching for 'webcams' on The Wildlife Trusts' website.

10 POINTS

Broken eggshell

By the end of spring you might be able to spy a broken, empty eggshell on the ground or in an empty nest.

30 POINTS

nimal behaviours

ere is a lot of animal behaviour to look out for during spring. Some
ecies are waking up from hibernation while others are breeding.

Great spotted woodpecker drumming

Listen carefully when you're in woodland during late
winter and early spring, and you might hear
the sound of a woodpecker drumming its
beak against a tree. The knocking sound
is repeated rapidly for short bursts, and
is done to attract a mate and claim territory.
Score double points if you see one.

20 POINTS

Great crested grebes courting

These elegant-looking water birds do an elaborate dance together as part of their courting routine before they mate in early spring. It involves them weaving, bobbing and swimming parallel to each other, and at the end they appear to run on the surface of the water. Look for them on lakes, reservoirs and rivers.

4 POIN

TOP SPOT!

Skylark singing

From March onwards, you can hear this small bird singing its chirruping song as it hovers high up in the air above open countryside. It may be tricky to see the skylark, though you might see it plummeting back down to the ground when it has finished singing.

20 POINTS

Hedgehog waking up from hibernation

Hedgehogs come out of hibernation in March or April. You might see them out looking for food in the evenings as they wake up very hungry! They can travel up to two miles each night in search of food, but you could help them by leaving out some meaty cat food and water to drink.

25 POINTS

Animal behaviours

Stoat bounding

A stoat is an orangey-brown mammal with a cream-coloured belly and a long, black-tipped tail. Its total length is about 30 cm. Look out for them in grassland, heathland, woodland and river banks, though they move very quickly, arching their backs as they bound along.

3 POINTS

Lamb feeding

When young lambs feed from their mothers, you can tell that they are getting some milk because their tails wiggle.

20 POINTS

Bat swooping

Bats come out of hibernation in April. They are very active after dusk for the rest of the spring, swooping to catch flies in mid-air. If they fly close to your head, don't worry! They're not going to crash into you, as they have a sophisticated way of navigating around objects in the dark.

20 POINTS

Squirrels chasing

Look out for squirrels chasing each other up, down and around trees as part of their courtship routine before they mate. Squirrels can have two litters a year, so you might spy them chasing in late winter/early spring, and again towards the end of spring. You are more likely to see grey squirrels than red ones, since grey squirrels are much more common.

10 POINTS

Animal behaviours

Peacock displaying

A peacock is a male peafowl. It has richly coloured plumage and long tail feathers which it fans out in a spectacular display to try and attract a mate. These birds aren't native to the UK, so look out for them in farm parks, stately homes and aviaries.

50 POINTS

TOP SPOT!

Buzzards circling

These large birds of prey are often seen in pairs or family groups, circling in the air over woodland and farmland. They announce their presence with an eery call, which some people mistake for a cat. Buzzards are brown and their wings are rounded at the end.

Dawn chorus

You'll have to be up early to hear the dawn chorus! It's one of the first signs of spring, when birds such as blackbirds, robins and song thrushes sing as the sun rises. They do this to attract a mate and defend their territory.

Hares boxing

In March or April, on farmland and open grassland, female hares fight off the males who want to mate with them by standing on their hind legs and 'boxing' with their front paws. The best time to see them is early in the morning or at dusk.

50 POINTS

TOP SPOT!

Caterpillar munching

Once caterpillars hatch out of
butterfly and moth eggs, they
get busy eating! They feed
on leaves, with each type of
caterpillar usually having a
preference for a particular plant.
Score 15 points for any type of
caterpillar you see munching its
way through a leaf.

15
POINTS

Peacock butterfly feeding

This butterfly is one of the earliest to
appear in spring, after hibernating
all winter. It feeds off
flower nectar in gardens,
parks, hedgerows
and woodland.
The markings on its
wings are there to scare
off predators, as they
look like big eyes!

20
POINTS

Animal behaviours

Shorn sheep

Look out for sheep that have had their coats shorn (cut very short), which happens in late spring. The fleece is usually sold for wool, but the shearing is also done to help keep the sheep healthy.

 20 POINTS

Honey bee gathering pollen

Once the spring flowers and blossoms come out, so do the honey bees. They fly from flower to flower, collecting pollen and nectar to take back to their colony.

 5 POINTS

Pond fish swimming

Ornamental fish such as goldfish, koi carp and golden orfe spend the cold winter months at the bottom of fish ponds, where the water is warmer. As the weather warms up, you will see them swimming around just beneath the surface, where there is more oxygen.

15 POINTS

Roe deer browsing

Roe deer are woodland animals, but in April and May you might see them eating at field edges. Roe deer 'browse', which means they eat the new shoots and leaves of plants, trees and crops.

50 POINTS

TOP SPOT!

Festivals, traditions and culture

There are several festivals and traditions associated with spring.
See how many of these you can spy.

World Book Day

This annual event takes place on the first Thursday in March.
You might see someone going to school dressed as their
favourite character from a book, or see an item about
World Book Day on a news programme. Or perhaps
you'll visit a library or read a book at home.
Score 10 points for any one of these.

10 POINTS

Mother's Day is an opportunity to thank our mums for everything they do for us. It takes place in more than 50 countries around the world, although they don't all celebrate it at the same time of year. Mothering Sunday is always celebrated three weeks before Easter in the UK and Ireland. Look out for these typical Mother's Day gifts.

Card

5 POINTS

Chocolates

5 POINTS

Bunch of flowers

5 POINTS

Festivals, traditions and culture

National flag

Three of the UK's patron saints are celebrated during spring: St David (Wales) on 1 March, St Patrick (Northern Ireland) on 17 March and St George (England) on 23 April. The patron saint of Scotland is St Andrew and St Andrew's Day is celebrated on 30 November. Score for any flag you see from a UK nation, including Scotland's.

10 POINTS

Clocks changing

On the last Sunday in March, the clocks go forward one hour. This has been done since the First World War in order to make the most of the daylight between March and October. Score for changing the time on any clock.

5 POINTS

Flower show

As more flowers come into bloom during spring, there might be a flower show near you, or you might find a spring event at a nearby garden centre.

30 POINTS

Festivals, traditions and culture

The Christian festival of Easter falls on a Sunday between 22 March and 25 April. The exact date depends on when the first full Moon of spring is. Whichever date it is on, one thing that doesn't change is that it is celebrated with chocolate!

Easter egg

◯ **5** POINTS

Mini eggs

◯ **5** POINTS

Chocolate bunny

◯ **5** POINTS

Chocolate lamb

◯ **10** POINT

Easter egg hunt

Looking for Easter chocolates around the house, garden or park is a fun thing to do on Easter Sunday. How many will you find?

10 POINTS

Easter bonnet

Hats have traditionally been decorated at Easter as a sign of the change of season and the new clothes that go with it. If you can't find an Easter bonnet, you could try decorating a hat yourself with flowers, ribbons, eggs, chicks or anything else you want!

10 POINTS

Painted eggs

Decorating hard-boiled eggs is a fun Easter craft to do.
You could dye them using food colouring, paint
them using watercolour or acrylic paints, and
glue on sequins, ribbons or buttons.

10 POINTS

Passover

The Jewish festival of Passover usually occurs in March or April, depending on when the spring full Moon is. The main part of the celebration is a meal, where a special type of bread called matzah (or matzo – see below) is eaten. Score 30 points for any reference to Passover that you see, including matzah or matzo in a supermarket.

30 POINTS

Festivals, traditions and culture

May Day

The first day of May has been traditionally celebrated as a festival of spring, although this is now sometimes observed on the first Monday of May, which is a bank holiday. Score points for any festival, fair or rally that you see taking place on 1 May or the bank holiday weekend.

20 POINTS

Folk dancers

Maypole and Morris dancing are two traditional dances associated with May Day, but you can score for any type of folk dance that you see or take part in during spring.

35 POINTS

ood

ok out for food which is traditionally eaten during spring or which
in season at this time of year. If you don't see it growing in a field
being prepared, look out for it in a shop, restaurant or market.

Leeks

Leeks are grown
in rows in fields,
their green leaves
showing above the
surface.

 5 POINTS

Spring greens

These are the first cabbages of
the year, with dark green leaves
that are soft and sweet
to eat. They are
very good
for you.

 15 POINTS

Spring onions

Spring onions can be grown all
year round, but originally they
were the first onions to appear
after the winter.

 5 POINTS

New potatoes

Young potatoes that are harvested while they are still small are known as new potatoes. They grow in the soil with just the green plant showing above ground.

5 POINTS

Grapefruit

These large citrus fruits are grown on trees in warm, tropical countries, so you are very unlikely to see them growing in the UK. They are available all year round in shops here, but are at their best in spring, which is when they are naturally in season.

10 POINTS

Rhubarb

Rhubarb grows as a long, slim stem with a large flat leaf at the top. It is easy to grow, so you might see it in a garden or on an allotment, and is ready for picking in spring.

15 POINTS

Food

Asparagus

Asparagus shoots grow out of the ground and are ready for cutting at the end of April. The shoots can grow very fast – up to 10 cm in one day! Look out for locally grown asparagus in farm shops and market stalls.

15 POINTS

Spring rolls

These Chinese snacks are traditionally eaten at spring festivals, which is how they got their name. They consist of a pancake filled with vegetables and meat which is rolled up tightly and deep fried. You will find them in supermarkets and Chinese takeaways and restaurants.

10 POINTS

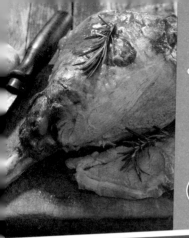

Lamb

Lamb that is eaten is the meat of a sheep under one year old. Spring lamb is often served as a roast dinner, but it is also popular in shepherd's pies, curries, burgers, and Greek and Middle Eastern dishes. Score for seeing lamb in a shop, on a menu or on a plate in front of you!

 10 POINTS

Crab

Edible crabs are in season from April onwards. The meat from the body part of the crab is brown, while the meat from the claws is white. Score for seeing crab meat from a fishmonger's or supermarket.

 15 POINTS

Food

Hot cross bun

These spiced bread rolls have a cross on the top and are traditionally easten at Easter. They are lovely toasted and spread with butter. Score an extra 10 points if you bake some yourself.

5 POINTS

Clothes

Spring weather can be changeable, so there should be plenty of opportunities to spot these different items of clothing while you are out and about.

Raincoat

5 POINTS

Wellies

5 POINTS

Clothes

On some spring days it's warm enough to wear shorts and a t-shirt, and to put on sandals. On other days, you might need a cardigan, coat and gloves!

Shorts ◯ **5** POINTS

T-shirt

◯ **5** POINTS

Cardigan

10 POINTS

Sandals

5 POINTS

Clothes

Gloves ◯ **5** POINTS

Dress

◯ **5** POINTS

Index

i-SPY How to get your i-SPY certificate and badge

Let us know when you've become a super-spotter with 1000 points and we'll send you a special certificate and badge!

Here's what to do:

- Ask an adult to check your score.

- Apply for your certificate at www.collins.co.uk/i-SPY (if you are under the age of 13 we'll need a parent or guardian to do this).

- We'll email your certificate and post you a brilliant badge!